This book belongs to

This book is dedicated to my
very own Frankie, who is fabulous
in every way.

Acknowledgements

A huge thank you to Rob for your constant love and support. Thanks to my three amazing children who inspire me to write these stories. Many thanks to TAUK Kids and Fountain Creative for helping me create this beautiful book. Lulu, thank you for supporting and inspiring me. Special thanks to Andrew, who has, yet again, created the most wonderful illustrations.

Fabulous Frankie's Huge Heart

By Jessica Bowers

Illustrated by Andrew Whitehead

First published in 2022 by Jessica Bowers Well-being Writer

Copyright Jessica Bowers © 2022
All rights reserved.

ISBN: 978-1-3999-2997-4

This is the second in the author's *Fantastic Fin and Friends* series supporting children's mental health.

Written by
Jessica Bowers

FABULOUS FRANKIE'S

HUGE HEART

BOOK 2

Illustrated by Andrew Whitehead

Fabulous Frankie has a huge heart
which aches when it is time to part
with things she holds precious and dear;

she wants to
keep them
very near.

A broken toy,
a holey sock,
a clock that's lost
its ticky tock.

Recycling that
she keeps for art,
a used behaviour
sticker chart.

Her lip quivers,
and she looks glum
at clear-out time
with Dad and Mum.

It causes
problems, it is true,
as they do not
know what to do.

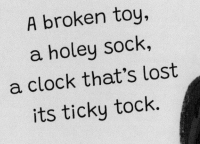
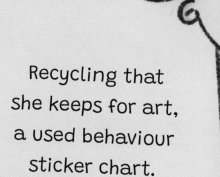

Fabulous Frankie hears a sound.
Her mouth gapes when she looks around
to see the most beautiful sight
in front of her, shining so bright.

She rubs her eyes, then has a blink,
a fairy smiles and gives a wink and says,
"My name is Fairy Nice.
I've come to offer some advice."

"Your heart's so big
and that is why,
you can let go of this pigsty.

The things we love
stay in our heart,
like pictures of most
precious art."

Then Fabulous Frankie
closed her eyes
and met with
a lovely surprise.

Precious pictures
of all the things
she loves with all
the joy they bring.

Her broken toy, her holey sock,
her clock that lost its ticky tock.

Recycling that she keeps for art, her used behaviour sticker chart.

GOING IN THE BIN

Soon the penny
finally drops.

"It's not about
all of the props!
My happiness comes
from within,
the rubbish can
go in the bin!"

She's thankful for the lovely things,
but knows the joy
her heart can bring.

High5

CRACK

ZOOM

WHIZZ

Then Fairy Nice did
warmly say,
"And that's my cue to
fly away!"

Frankie helps Mum
give things away,
and bags the
rubbish for bin day.

Charity Shop
SALE

frankie's
keep Sakes

She keeps only a little box,
of memories, not holey socks,
(and maybe a few sticks
and rocks).

recycle
help the planet

The rest she treasures deep inside,
memories make her smile so wide.
Fabulous Frankie has a huge heart,
which holds things dear when they do part.

Fabulous Frankie has a huge heart,
which also aches when she's apart
from all her friends and family.
Together she prefers to be.

Following time spent with her friends,
she feels upset towards the end.
She finds it hard to say goodbye,
on leaving, she just wants to cry.

Her voice wavers
before she weeps,
she's still sad
when she goes to sleep.

Mum and Dad start
splitting hairs,
they feel helpless
with despair.

At night she dreams of those goodbyes,

Fairy Nice appears and dries her eyes.

She whispers wisdom in her ear, and Frankie's sadness disappears.

Fabulous Frankie wakes with glee,
with loved ones in her memory.
She feels her love fill up inside,
her huge heart swells with great pride.

Fabulous Frankie has a huge heart,
which holds those dear when they do part.

FABULOUS FRANKIE'S GOODBYE GUIDE!

⭐ Remember that it is normal to feel sad when we say goodbye.

⭐ These feelings will pass.

⭐ Let someone know how you feel so they can help you.

⭐ A big hug might help – if no one is around, then place two loving hands on your heart and take some deep breaths.

⭐ You could draw a picture or write a story to express your feelings.

⭐ Do something you love to help you feel happy. You might want to listen to music, dance, play a game or go outside. We can feel sad and happy at the same time.

THINK POSITIVELY...

💜 Feel proud when you give away things that you no longer use. Someone else will enjoy them, just like you did.

💜 When you give away things you no longer need, you create space for something lovely and new.

💜 You can use your imagination and memories to picture your loved ones whenever you like.

💜 Your heart is huge and holds all the love that you have for everyone and everything.

Remember, Fairy Nice says:

"The love you feel stays in your heart; from that love, you will never part!"

Fill this huge heart with the things that you love.

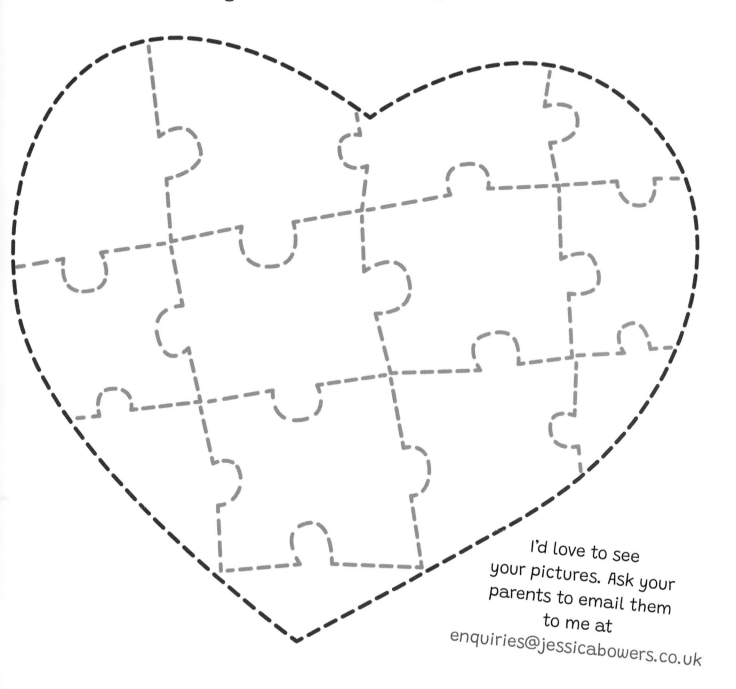

I'd love to see your pictures. Ask your parents to email them to me at enquiries@jessicabowers.co.uk

FAIRY NICE'S GUIDE

Being N.I.C.E. means:
Niceness Is Chosen Every day.

I agree to be NICE to:

Others
★ I will smile at someone every day.
★ I will be kind to others.
★ I will offer help when I can.

Myself
★ I will be kind to myself.
★ I will ask for help when I need it.
★ I will do at least one thing I love every day.

The World
★ I will give old toys and clothes away.
★ I will recycle to help the planet.
★ I will not litter and will throw away my rubbish.

YOUR NAME HERE!

Signed _____

Signed

TIPS FOR PARENTS:
SUPPORTING ENDINGS AND GOODBYES

⭐ **Normalise their feelings** — Reassure your children that their feelings are perfectly normal and will pass.

⭐ **Don't try to fix it** — Instead, be the container for their feelings by listening with acceptance and care. Time and space always help.

⭐ **Ask them** — What do they need to support them at this time?

⭐ **Get creative** — Writing or artwork may enable them to express themselves if they struggle to put their feelings into words.

⭐ **Cultivate warm, positive memories** — You can help your little one decorate a jar or box to hold their special keepsakes in, make a scrapbook of good times or create a photobook of their loved ones.

⭐ **Self-Care** — Suggest an activity that they might like to do. You could go for a walk, read a book, or play a game together. Let your little ones know that they can feel sad about something and still enjoy other things at the same time.

ABOUT THE AUTHOR

Jessica Bowers is a children's author and well-being writer with an extensive background in supporting mental health and well-being. Jessica has a counselling and psychotherapy practice based in Derbyshire. She is passionate about supporting and enhancing good mental health in children. Jessica lives with her lovely husband, three wonderful children and two tortoises!

www.jessicabowers.co.uk

f @jessicabowerswellbeingwriter

◎ @jessicabowerswellbeingwriter

𝕏 @bowerswellbeing

ABOUT THE ILLUSTRATOR

Andrew Whitehead is an experienced illustrator of 25 years who developed a very early interest in all things artistic - since 6 to be precise.

Inspired by the vibrancy of 80s pop culture and the scribbles of Tinker Hatfield, Andrew pursued his career in illustration and now showcases appearances with worldwide enterprises such as *Arsenal*, *Yamaha*, *McDonalds*, *Pizza Express* and *Speedo*.

Clients often commission Andrew for his engaging, lively and dynamic illustrations that truly bring life to the every day. From start to finish Andrew works closely with writers and editors to ensure their vision is turned from the written word to a visual reality.

www.since6.co.uk

Printed in Great Britain
by Amazon

32697202R00018